Date Due

WILD FOLK
at the Pond

Other books by Carroll Lane Fenton

LIFE LONG AGO: THE STORY OF FOSSILS

ALONG THE HILL

EARTH'S ADVENTURES:
THE STORY OF GEOLOGY FOR YOUNG PEOPLE

ALONG NATURE'S HIGHWAY

WEEJACK AND HIS NEIGHBORS

WILD FOLK
at the Pond

BY CARROLL LANE FENTON

ILLUSTRATIONS
BY THE AUTHOR

The John Day Company, New York

CONTENTS

TO PARENTS AND TEACHERS

This is the second book in a series telling the stories of animals that live in varied surroundings, or habitats. The stories also mention a few plants, for animals could not live where they do if plants were not present.

The first book in the series, *Weejack and His Neighbors,* deals with creatures that are common on farms, in woods and vacant lots, and even in city parks. The animals to be met in this volume, however, are found in or near ponds and the creeks that flow to them. With the plants among which they live, these creatures form what scientists call an *ecologic* association, or community.

Many different things belong to the pond community. We encounter some lowly ones such as clams and snails, as well as insects, crayfish, and several kinds of animals that have vertebrae, or backbones. Each one represents an important group of living things and an important way of living. Thus Es-see Raccoon is cared for by his mother, but Croaker Green Frog grows up without even knowing who his parents are. Graywing, the heron, hunts food for himself and his nestlings, but the mussel takes whatever comes in the water she brings into her body. Turtles and dragonflies have no special home, but Diver and red-winged blackbirds build nests, while kingfishers dig a tunnel and an underground room in which they rear their young.

In short, *Wild Folk at the Pond* introduces boys and girls to important groups in the animal kingdom and to typical

7

ways of life in or near the water. Two children appear in several of the stories, suggesting that young readers may find both enjoyment and knowledge by observing wild creatures.

Vocabulary, sentence structure, and content have been adjusted to the needs of boys and girls who will want to do their own reading. The stories also may be read aloud to children five to seven years of age.

WILD FOLK
at the Pond

ADVENTURES OF ES-SEE RACCOON

Es-see opened his black eyes and yawned. He had slept all day long. Now he was ready to wake up and watch for his mother.

Es-see was a baby raccoon, only three weeks old. He had grayish-brown fur, with two black spots on his face. Rings of black and brownish white ran around his tail.

The little raccoon had one brother and two sisters. They looked so much alike that only their mother could tell them apart. Their black eyes and the black spots on their faces made them look very happy. They always seemed to be smiling, even when they were asleep!

Es-see's home was a hole in a willow tree that stood beside a pond. There he and his brother and sisters stayed for several weeks. When their mother went away from the hole, they snuggled down and slept. When she came home, they woke up and drank her warm milk. Then they went to sleep again.

When the little raccoons felt very daring, they went to the door of their home and peeped out. But they did not leave the hole, for Mother had told them not to. She had not told them in words, of course, for raccoons are not able to talk. Instead, she sniffed and pushed them back when they put their heads out of the door. "Go back!" her sniffs and pushes meant. "Little raccoons must never go away from home."

One evening Es-see forgot what his mother had told him. He looked out of the door and saw a moth, sitting on a twig. He reached for it, but it flew to a twig that was farther away. Es-see slipped out of the door and started to follow the moth.

The little coon took step after step as the moth went farther and farther. At last he came to the end of a branch. Es-see sat looking down on the pond, which was under him. There were many

trees on its bank. A creek flowed into one end of the pond, but the other end was swampy. Cattails and plants called arrowheads grew in the swampy place. Pond lilies with bright yellow buds grew where the water was deeper.

Es-see sat on the branch till a crow said, "Caw! Caw!" loudly. Then he turned and tried to go back to his hole. But one paw slipped, and then another. Down he fell into the water under the willow tree!

Es-see had never fallen before, but he seemed to know just what to do. He twisted and turned in the air, landing on all four feet. In a moment he waded out of the water and stood on the dry, leafy ground.

The little raccoon looked up into the tree, which seemed much bigger than it ever had been before. It was so big that Es-see could not climb it, though he tried again and again. His toes lost their hold every time, and he tumbled back to the ground.

Es-see looked for his mother, who always

knew just what to do. When he could not find her he started to whimper. "Ee-er, Ee-er-er!" he cried in a voice like the chirping of a bird.

Mother Raccoon was away in the woods when Es-see began to whimper. She stopped and sat up to listen with her wide, pointed ears. One of her little ones was in trouble! In a moment she started home at a gallop, as fast as her short legs would go.

Es-see tried to snuggle close to her when she came to the tree. But Mother did not feel like snuggling. Instead, she picked Es-see up and put him on the tree, between her own front paws. She pushed and guided while he scrambled up, and caught him when he slipped. When he whimpered, she nudged him with her nose. "Go on," her nudges seemed to say. "There's nothing to be afraid of when I'm here to help!"

At last Es-see scrambled through the door. By this time he was tired, as well as dry enough to lie down with his brother and sisters. Mother gave all four a drink of milk and went to find her own supper. She knew that Es-see would not forget and run away again.

When the month of July came, all the young raccoons were big enough to leave their home. While Mother watched, they climbed up and down the willow tree and ran about on the ground. They wrestled, played tag, and ran races from one tree to another.

Indeed, the babies became so strong that Mother Raccoon decided to give them a Fourth of July picnic. First, she taught them to walk behind her and not to lag or wander away. Then she led them to a log that had fallen into the swampy part of the pond. When they got there, the young ones sat on the bank while their mother walked to the edge of the water and fished for frogs.

She fished by keeping perfectly still until a frog came near. Then she reached out quickly and caught it with her paw.

The frog was clean, for it lived in the water. But that made no difference to Mother Raccoon.

She scrubbed it, thumped it with her paws, and then scrubbed it again. Finally, she picked off pieces of tender white meat and gave them to her children. Every little coon washed its piece before taking a bite!

A few weeks later, the raccoon family had a different kind of picnic. They went from their home tree to a cornfield, where Mother Raccoon showed her children how to peel the green husks from roasting ears. Es-see got silk between his toes, and had to pull it out. But he soon learned to eat the sweet, soft kernels. He thought corn was better than frog meat or any other food. He would always be ready when Mother wanted to go on a green-corn picnic!

While Es-see was eating, Mother Raccoon heard a noise. "Bow-wow!" it came, growing louder and louder. The farmer's dog was coming to chase the raccoons away from his master's corn!

Mother knew just what to do. In two jumps she started back to the woods, with the little ones close behind her. When they came to a tall tree they stopped, and Mother turned toward them. "Climb quickly, children!" she seemed to say. "Don't stop to wait for me!"

Es-see scrambled up the tree, and so did his brother and sisters. Mother came last of all. Indeed, she stayed on the ground till the dog was just a few feet away. Then she climbed up to the young coons. All five of them sat side by side on the branch, looking down at the dog.

"Bow-wow!" he barked again and again, jumping against the tree. But he did not know how to climb, and the raccoons would not come down. At last the dog got tired of barking. He turned away, growled a few times, and then trotted back to the farm.

The young raccoons began to fidget, but Mother made them wait until she could not hear the dog, or smell him with her sharp nose. Then she sniffed and led the way to the ground.

The little ones wanted to go back to the cornfield, but Mother Raccoon would not let them.

The dog would chase them away again—and besides, it was time to go back to their hole in the willow tree.

When they got there, the young raccoons snuggled down and soon began to yawn. They fell asleep, one after another, until only Es-see was awake. He yawned and blinked at Mother, who was sitting at the door.

What a fine, exciting night it had been! And how good that corn had tasted, even though the farmer's dog had made them stop eating it!

TURTLES IN THE POND

Snapper was lying in the pond, near the log where Es-see's mother sometimes hunted frogs. His brown shell was covered with mud and green plants, which made it look like a large, rough stone. His head looked like a smaller stone lying beside the large one.

Stones, of course, are not alive—but Snapper was a living snapping turtle. He also was awake and hungry. When a minnow swam toward him, he watched until it came close. Then out shot his head and snap! went his jaws, which were almost as sharp as knives. They cut the minnow into two pieces. Snapper swallowed one piece after the other. Then he blinked his eyes and lay still again.

After a while he decided to hunt, instead of waiting for food to come to him. So he swam

into shallow water and poked about, trying to stir up some frogs. If he had found one he would have caught it before it could jump away.

The big turtle had another way of hunting that made him dangerous to birds swimming in the pond. He would slip quietly along underwater until he could rush up and catch a bird by its feet. Then he sank to the bottom again, holding his prey until it drowned. When it was dead he would have a meal of bird meat, which seemed to taste better than minnows or the flesh of frogs.

Although Snapper could walk on dry land if he had to, he almost never went away from the pond. His four webbed feet were just right for swimming, and he could not swallow food when his head was out of water. His legs were very short, too. They could hardly lift his shell and his big, fat body, which weighed more than thirty pounds.

One morning Snapper felt restless and began to swim to and fro. He went from the log to a place where the water was deep, and then came back toward the shore. At last he found his mate, Mrs. Snapper. She was lying quietly on the bottom, in a tangle of weeds and dead stems.

Snapper looked at Mrs. Snapper, blinking his little eyes. Then he stopped swimming and settled down beside her, without making a sound.

The big turtles remained near one another, though they never seemed to become friendly.

At last, soon after the Fourth of July, Mother Snapper left her mate and took a trip on land. She crawled up the bank and under the trees till she came to some bare, sandy soil. There she scraped the soil away with her feet, making a shallow hole.

This hole was Mrs. Snapper's nest. She wriggled and pushed her body into it and remained there while she laid two dozen round eggs that had white, hard shells. Then she covered the eggs with dirt and dead leaves. After pressing these down with her feet, she crawled back to the pond.

Mother Snapper's eggs lay in the hole until they hatched. The baby snapping turtles had rough shells, big heads, and long, thin tails. After digging their way out of the nest, they walked around in the sunshine. At first they went in every direction, but they soon began to crawl toward the pond. When they got there, every one of them started to swim and hunt worms or insects for lunch. They seemed to be every bit as hungry as their father and mother, whom they had never seen.

Perhaps you have already decided that Snapper and Mrs. Snapper were lonely, fierce creatures that never made friends with their neighbors. Ruth and Bobby decided so, too, when they learned to look into the water and tell the snapping turtles from stones.

Ruth and Bobby often came to the pond, for their father owned the land around it, and they lived a short distance away. Father showed them Es-see's hole, and tracks that the raccoons made in mud beside the water. He told them how much fun it would be to make friends with creatures that lived in and near the pond.

"But don't try to make friends with Snapper," said Father, "for snapping turtles just aren't friendly. They spend most of their lives alone, and they live on things that they catch by biting fast and hard. If you were to put your finger near Snapper he'd bite it, just as if it were something to eat."

"I'll bet he'd hurt, too!" said Bobby.

"He certainly would hurt!" Father answered. "Here—push this stick close to his nose and notice how hard he bites it. Just suppose he were biting your finger instead of a piece of dead wood!"

Ruth and Bobby kept away from Snapper, but they always were glad to see Dorsa, who also lived in the pond. Though people often called her a mud turtle, she really was a painted turtle, or painted terrapin. Her shell was greenish black on top, with a border of red and black. The under part of her shell was yellow, without any markings at all.

One day Ruth spied a new kind of turtle near the edge of the pond. Its plump-looking oval shell was dull, muddy brown on top and dark yellow on the underside. Its head was large for the size of its body, and was pointed much like Snapper's. When the turtle saw a wriggling worm in the water, it reached out and bit quickly, just as Snapper did.

"Still, it isn't a snapping turtle," Ruth de-

cided. "Its shell is not rough like Snapper's, and it doesn't have the right shape."

"It's not a mud turtle, either," Bobby told her. "Look at those yellow stripes on its head—most mud turtles have spots. And the shell on the underside of its body is not nearly wide enough to be a mud turtle's!"

The creature really was a musk turtle. It got that name because it made a strong odor when it was alarmed or annoyed. This caused its enemies to drop it very quickly.

The musk turtle seemed to hear Ruth and Bobby talking. It turned and looked at them for a moment, and then it swam away. Soon it dived toward the bottom of the pond—but just then it saw Snapper, watching and ready to bite. Swish! went the musk turtle's webbed feet, as it turned back toward the surface and quickly swam away.

There was plenty of room to swim about and hunt for food in other parts of the pond. Musk Turtle did not want to stay near cross, hungry Snapper, who might bite off one of his legs!

FAIRIES AND A WATER TIGER

A mother fairy shrimp was swimming in a tiny pool near the pond. She was pinkish brown and about one inch long. She had eleven pairs of jointed, feathery legs. She waved her legs to and fro as she swam through the pool on her back.

As Mother Fairy swam about, she began to lay her eggs. They were tiny balls, held together in strings of tough jelly. Mother Fairy did not make a nest for them, or even fasten them to dead leaves. Instead, she let her egg-strings sink to the bottom of the pool.

Long before summer came, water in the pool dried up. The eggs dried up, too, and lay on the ground. Wind blew many of them away. It took some to low places in the woods, and some to the very edge of the pond.

When autumn arrived, rains fell and filled the

low places. Rains also made the pond larger. In time, shallow water covered the place where Mother Fairy's eggs were lying.

In winter, the shallow water grew cold. At last it froze into ice, which did not melt until spring.

Freezing kills many things, but it did not harm the eggs. They lived in the ice all through the winter and hatched soon after it melted, in the month of March.

At first the baby fairy shrimps were short, with only a few jointed legs. They also were very tiny—so tiny that Ruth and Bobby could not see them in the water at the edge of the pond.

The young fairy shrimps were hungry, too, as most babies are. Since they were too small to catch worms or insects, they had to eat little things that floated in the water. They ate so much that they changed and grew very rapidly. Soon they were shaped like their mother, and were almost a half inch long.

"They don't look like their mother," said

Water Tiger

Bobby, when the fairy shrimps were big enough to be seen. "She was brown, but most of her babies are pale green or white. Some of them are pink, too, with white on their legs and tails. I guess fairy shrimps can be 'most any color!"

As the fairy shrimps grew up, they became much easier to see. Soon both Ruth and Bobby noticed that they were not quite alike. Some had horn-shaped things on their heads; these were the fathers, or males. The mothers, or females, had no "horns," but they did have two round or oval pouches behind their last pair of legs. The mothers kept their eggs in these pouches until they were ready to lay.

One day, while Ruth and Bobby were watching the fairy shrimps, they discovered a water tiger. He looked like a white, jointed, six-legged worm as he crawled over sticks and dead leaves. He really was a young beetle of a kind that lives in the water until it becomes full grown.

"He's just a beetle baby," Ruth told Bobby. "He doesn't look like a tiger at all. I wonder why he got that name!"

She found out when Bobby put the water tiger into a jar with a fairy shrimp. The tiger sat still while the fairy swam about, but as soon as it settled down to rest he began to creep toward it. Closer and closer he came, until he could jump upon the fairy and bite it with his sharp jaws.

"He does act like a tiger, after all," Ruth decided. "Do you suppose he spends his whole time hunting fairies and insects to eat?"

The water tiger ate by sucking with his jaws. In a short time, the fairy shrimp's thin shell was empty. Instead of resting, the tiger began to crawl about. "He wants more to eat," Ruth told Bobby. "But don't you dare feed him another fairy shrimp!"

"I won't," Bobby promised. "I'll give him some wrigglers. There—he's got one already!

"Mr. Water Tiger must be hungry all the time. Ruth, I'm getting hungry, too. Let's put our tiger back into the pond and go home to supper!"

THE KINGFISHER FAMILY

"Look, Bobby!" Ruth whispered one morning in the spring. "There's a kingfisher perched on that high bank beside our pond. He is pecking and scratching at the dirt."

"Sure. He's digging a hole for his nest," Bobby answered. "Let's sit down to watch him."

The children sat and watched until they were tired, but the kingfisher kept on digging. Peck! Peck! Peck! went his big, strong beak against the dirt in the bank, prying out pebbles and lumps of soil. At first they rolled into the water. But in an hour the hole was so deep that the kingfisher had to stop pecking and push the pebbles out of the door.

At last Father Kingfisher stopped digging. He shook the dust from his feathers and perched

on a root that stuck out of the bank. There he stayed until Mother Kingfisher came to take her turn at digging.

Mother Kingfisher had a gray-blue back and tail, with spots and short bars of white. Her neck and throat were white, too, and there was a white spot in front of each eye. The rest of her head was gray-blue, with a black streak in the feathers of her crest. She could raise these feathers when she wished, making her crest stand up stiffly.

On her breast was a grayish blue band, which made many people call her a *belted* kingfisher. Below the blue belt was a reddish one, and there were brown feathers on her sides. Father Kingfisher looked just like his mate, except that he had only one belt—the grayish blue one—and his sides had the same color.

Mother Kingfisher hopped into the hole and began to make it deeper. Where the soil was soft, she could dig rapidly. Where the soil was hard, she dug slowly. In one place, the soil was so hard that she had to peck and pry to break it. Some of the stones were so sharp that they scratched her strong beak.

Day after day both birds worked, though Father Kingfisher did more digging than Mother. At last their hole became a tunnel six feet long. It sloped upward from the door, so that rain could not run into it. At the end of the tunnel was a round room about as big as a football. When the kingfishers dug that room, they had to push stones and dirt all the way down their tunnel and out through the door.

The birds did not work all the time, of course. Sometimes they sat on branches to rest and to clean their dusty feathers. When they were hungry, they went fishing in the pond, or in a creek that flowed into it. Usually while one bird was getting something to eat, the other was busy digging.

Father Kingfisher liked to fish by perching on a branch that hung far out over the water. When he tipped his head to one side, his keen eyes could see into the water, keeping watch for young bullheads, minnows, and frogs. When he saw one, he dived and caught it with his beak. Then he shook the water from his feathers and flew to his perch to eat. He liked to swallow fish headfirst, without dividing them into pieces. Some of the largest fish would hardly go down his throat!

Mother Kingfisher sometimes fished from a branch, but she also liked to fly. She could hover above the water, moving her wings very fast. When she saw a fish, she would dive. If the fish swam away or dodged, she tried to follow it. Sometimes, of course, she missed. Then Mother Kingfisher would give an angry, rattling cry and start to hover again.

Even when the kingfishers weren't hungry they kept close watch on the part of the creek that was nearest the pond. They had picked out this part for their own, as a place in which to go fishing. A big rock in the water marked one end of their fishing ground, while a willow that stood on the bank marked the other end. They would not let any other kingfisher come between the rock and the willow. If a strange bird came near, they rattled angrily and drove him away.

Though the kingfishers guarded their part of the creek, they did not drive other birds away from the pond. The pond, you see, was not theirs. It belonged to all the kingfishers who wanted to come to it. Any bird might catch bullheads, tadpoles, and frogs in the pond without being driven away.

When the kingfishers finished the room at the end of the tunnel, both of them took a rest. Then they caught some minnows in the creek and two frogs in the pond. Minnows and frogs made such a big meal that they had to rest again.

Next morning, Mother Kingfisher came to the tunnel early. She went straight to the room at the end, nestled down, and laid a white egg on the floor.

Mother Kingfisher laid an egg every day for seven days. When the seventh egg was laid, she started to sit. When she became tired or hungry,

Father Kingfisher would take her place. He always seemed ready to sit on the eggs, keeping them safe and warm.

The kingfishers took turns sitting for seventeen days before the eggs began to hatch. Out came seven babies with big heads, no feathers, and bare red skins. Their eyes were tightly shut, and they huddled close together when their mother left the nest.

After a few days the kingfisher babies, or nestlings, began to grow feathers. But the feathers were not soft and fluffy, for each one was hidden away in a hard, gray case. Those cases stuck out from the bare skin and looked almost like spines.

When the young birds were twelve days old their eyes began to open. Six days later the sheaths popped off their feathers. In the morning the nestlings were rough and spiny, but when evening came they looked almost like their parents. They fluttered their stubby wings and raised the blue crests on their heads. When they sat up straight, some showed one blue band on the breast, like Father Kingfisher. Others had one blue band and one red one, just as their mother had.

For nine more days the young kingfishers stayed in their underground room, at the end of their long tunnel. They ate small fish and tadpoles that their parents brought them. They also grew rapidly. By the time they were one month old, they were almost as large as their parents.

One day, when both Father and Mother were away, the young kingfishers walked through the tunnel. The first one stuck his beak out of the tunnel, and the second peeped over his shoulder. The other five could not see out, but they did notice that bright sunlight came into the door. It was not at all like the darkness in which they had been living. It made them feel just a bit afraid, so they hurried back to their room.

Next morning the young birds went through the tunnel again. The first one stopped to blink at the sunshine, but the others kept right on coming. In a moment they began to push. They pushed so hard that the first nestling teetered and then tumbled out of the door. The next one came right behind him—and then the next, and the next. At last only a single nestling was left, sitting in the door.

As the young birds fell they moved their wings up and down, just as fast as they could. In a moment they began to fly. Off they fluttered to a long root that was sticking out of the bank. There they perched side by side, blinking their eyes in the sunlight. But when their father came with a minnow, each young bird opened his mouth for it. "Give it to *me!*" each one seemed to say. *"Give that minnow to ME!"*

Father Kingfisher hovered above the six young ones, and then gave the minnow to the one that had left the tunnel first. Then he flew back to catch some more food. As he left, Mother came with a frog.

The young bird sitting in the tunnel opened its mouth and begged. But Mother Kingfisher did not even look at it. She gave the frog to one of the young birds on the root and flew away again.

The lone nestling in the tunnel closed its mouth and watched her hungrily. Then it gave a queer little jump. Out of the doorway it popped, fluttering its wings so hard that it flew out over the pond. It had to turn and come back to the root where its brothers and sisters were sitting.

That was where Father found it when he came with another minnow. Once more all the young birds opened their mouths, but the one that had just come from the burrow opened its mouth widest of all. "Feed *me* this time!" it seemed to be saying. *"Feed me;* I'M HUN-GRY!"

FATHER BULLHEAD'S NEST

Two bullheads, or horned pouts, were swimming among the plants called arrowheads, which
grew near one end of the pond. The fish poked
their blunt noses between the stems and felt in
every corner. They had four feelers on their
chins and two above their noses. The feelers near
their mouths looked like long, thin mustaches.

The bullheads were trying to find a good place
for their nest. A muddy bottom would not do,
and they did not like places with dead sticks. One
spot was spoiled by water weeds which grew so
thickly that the bullheads could hardly swim
through them.

At last the two fish found a place that seemed
exactly right. It had a clean, gravelly bottom.
There were stems of arrowheads and cattails, but
almost no water weeds.

The nest was a saucer-shaped hollow about one foot in width. The bullheads dug it by sucking pebbles into their mouths and then carrying them away. Soon they opened their mouths, dropped the pebbles, and then swam back to get more. Since both father and mother fish worked together, they finished the nest in a short time.

When the last pebble was taken away, Mother Bullhead laid her eggs. Each egg was a little, round ball. Mother Bullhead laid hundreds and hundreds of those balls. Then she swam away to rest and to find some earthworms for supper.

Mother Bullhead was about fifteen inches long, but her mate was an inch or two shorter. Both had soft skins without any scales, blunt fins, and stubby tails. Their under parts were yellowish white, while their backs and sides were yellowish brown with dark splotches. They looked very much like mud on the bottom of the pond.

Although Father Bullhead was hungry, he did not leave the nest. Instead, he stayed just above it, moving his fins very slowly. But when

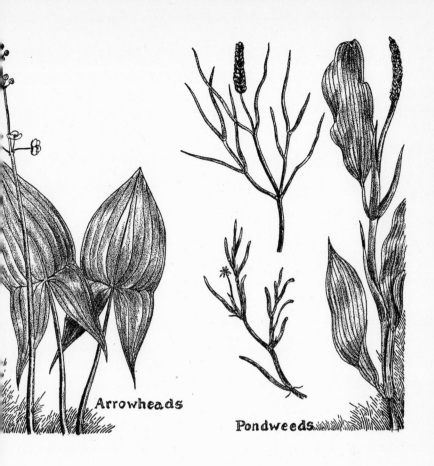

Arrowheads

Pondweeds

a sucker came near, the bullhead was not slow at all. He dashed at the sucker and drove it away, as fast as it could go. Then he hurried back to the nest and kept watch for other fish that might try to eat the eggs.

Mother Bullhead sometimes helped her mate

take care of the eggs. At other times she swam near the nest or rested among the stems of arrowheads and water lilies. But when the baby fish began to hatch, she did not pay much attention to them. In fact, Father Bullhead sometimes chased her away and took care of the baby fish himself.

Many things like to eat newly hatched fish, and Father Bullhead had to keep all such enemies away. He also had to see that the babies did not get lost and did not harm one another. When they swam out of the nest, he chased them back. When they crowded together, he stirred them up.

He did this by putting his chin close to the bottom and pointing all his feelers forward. Then he give a quick flip with his fins. His feelers would turn a whole crowd of babies topsy-turvy, so that those at the bottom came to the top. This gave them a chance to get pure, fresh water, which they needed to breathe and grow strong.

At last the baby fish became big enough to

swim away from the nest. They went in a flock, or "school," swimming round and round their father. They touched his feelers and bumped into his fins. They even bothered him when he ate. More than once, when he tried to swallow some food, two or three little fish swam right into his mouth. He had to stop swallowing and spit them out. Sometimes the food came out, too, so that Father Bullhead went hungry.

That did not make him angry, for it seemed quite natural. Besides, there were plenty of things to eat in the pond, and Father Bullhead soon caught another meal.

The little fish grew rapidly and began to take care of themselves. They hid among weeds when suckers came near, or when a hungry perch that lived in the pond tried to swallow them. They learned to catch tiny insects, and to eat little worms that wriggled on the bottom of the pond.

At last the young fish were able to take care of themselves. Instead of going one by one, they all left in a single afternoon. Father Bullhead stayed where he was for a while. Then he began to grub on the bottom. He gobbled down two snails, some insects, and a crayfish, and he also ate several worms. When he could not swallow another bite, he found a shady corner under some lily leaves. It would make a good place to stay the next day, unless he decided to take a sun bath above a gravelly bank.

Father Bullhead was going to take a rest, now that his children were big enough to care for themselves.

GRAY-WING AND MOTHER HERON

"Quosk? Quosk-quosk?" called Gray-wing as he awoke, long before the sun came up. "Quah! Qua-wah!" his mate answered. "Yes, it's time to awaken," she seemed to be saying. "Soon we'll have to find breakfast for our little ones."

Gray-wing and his mate were great blue herons, though people sometimes called them blue cranes. Their home was a large nest made of sticks, at the top of a tall, dead tree that stood near the pond. Two other herons had their nest in the same tree, and another pair lived in the one next to it. All these birds were so near that they woke up when Gray-wing called, "Quosk-quosk?"

Though the herons could tell each other apart, they looked very much alike. All had long legs, long necks, and long, yellow beaks. Their backs were bluish gray, but their wings and tails were darker, and their necks had brownish streaks. Their throats and the tops of their heads were white, but black stripes ran back from their eyes and ended in crests of thin, stiff feathers. The herons could raise these crests or keep them close to the backs of their necks.

As soon as Gray-wing was awake, he hopped to the topmost branch of the tree. There he stretched his long neck and tilted his head from one side to the other. When he did this, he could look down on the woods, the pond, and the creek that flowed into it. He could see fields and roads, too, and houses in which people lived. One house was the home of Ruth and Bobby, who still were sound asleep.

When Gray-wing tilted his head still more, he looked down on his own babies. They had long necks, long legs, and long beaks, like Gray-wing and Mother Heron. Their backs and sides were covered with bluish gray down, but their under parts were white.

The little herons had opened their eyes as soon as their mother stood up. Now they bobbed their heads and opened their mouths. "We are hungry!" they seemed to say. "Please give us something to eat!"

Mother Heron already knew what the little ones wanted. She stood at the edge of the nest, spread her wings, and flew to the other side of the pond. Gray-wing soon flew away, too. He went to the farthest end of the pond, where cattails and arrowheads were growing in the shallow water.

As Gray-wing flew from his tree, he showed that he was not a crane. Cranes fly with their legs straight out behind them and their necks stretched straight out ahead. Gray-wing's legs drooped, and his neck was bent so far back that his head almost touched his body. His broad wings made long, slow strokes that carried him through the air swiftly. Almost before he knew it, he came to the end of the pond.

When the big heron was ready to stop, he beat

his wings against the air, which made them work like brakes. He also straightened his neck and reached downward with his legs. In a moment he was standing in water that came almost to his "knees."

Gray-wing did not move again until the water stopped rippling around his legs. Then he began to wade through the pond, lifting his feet and putting them down ever so carefully. He also tilted his head to one side and then to the other while his eyes looked into the water. He could see anything that swam in it or that moved on the muddy bottom.

For a while not a single thing appeared—not even an insect or a tadpole. Then Gray-wing's toe touched a young bullfrog that was sitting among some arrowhead stems. It jumped up, swam a short distance, and then dived into the mud. But it did not dive very deeply, for its hind legs stuck out, showing just where it was.

Gray-wing watched the bullfrog's legs while he waded toward them. Soon he bent his neck into the shape of the letter S and then straightened it with a jerk. Down went his beak into the mud—and up it came like a flash, holding the careless bullfrog.

When Gray-wing caught fish or frogs for himself he always tossed them into the air, snapped them as they fell, and then swallowed them head-first. But this bullfrog was for his hungry nestlings. He hid it among some leaves on the bank and waded back into the pond.

Gray-wing stood a moment with his neck bent

back and his wings drooping. Then he straightened his neck and began to hunt for food again.

When Gray-wing spied some little fish, he stopped and stood perfectly still. Soon several fish swam straight toward him. Gray-wing caught one of them easily. He just managed to catch two more as they tried to swim away.

By that time the rest of the fish were hiding in a tangle of cattails. Gray-wing could not catch them there—and besides, his beak was full. Quickly he walked to the bank of the pond and laid the fish on the ground near the bullfrog. Then he picked all of them up and flew away to the nest.

Long before Gray-wing got there he could see the little herons bobbing their downy heads. They bobbed still harder when he perched on the nest, and they snatched at the food as soon as he laid it down. Two of them caught hold of one fish, tugging and jerking so hard that they finally pulled it in two!

Gray-wing watched while the little ones ate.

When the last piece of frog meat and fish had been swallowed, he got ready to fly away.

Just then he heard Mother Heron call, "Quah-wah!" and beat her wings against the water. Beat-splash! Beat-splash! went her wings. Something must be wrong!

Mother Heron had been fishing at the opposite side of the pond. She had caught several fish and had hidden them, and was trying to catch another. Nearer and nearer she came, watching the fish so closely that she did not see Snapper, the turtle, hiding in the mud. Out darted his head, and snap! went his sharp jaws, nipping one of her toes.

Mother Heron caught a glimpse of the turtle just in time to dodge. But dodging spoiled her balance, and she tumbled over. That was when she called, "Quah-wah!" She beat her wings against the water, too, as she tried to get up again.

The noise brought her mate, Gray-wing, as fast as he could come. It also alarmed a mother bittern that was standing on the bank of the

pond. She fluffed out her striped brown feathers and ran to her nest, which was hidden in tall grass and cattails. With her flashing eyes and open beak, she was ready to fight any enemy that might try to harm her babies!

Mother Heron did not even notice the bittern. She stood up and flew toward Gray-wing, as if she wanted to show him that she had not been hurt. Then she went to the place where her fish were hidden. With one snap of her beak she picked them up and carried them to her young ones.

Mother Heron laid the fish on the nest, just as Gray-wing had done. Next, she hopped to a limb near by and shook off some water that still clung to her feathers. Then she stood with her neck curved and her head between her shoulders.

Gray-wing stood on another branch, as if he were keeping watch. He saw two crows fly overhead and watched a broadwinged hawk that soared over a field. The hawk was hunting mice and ground squirrels, while the crows could not

Bittern

harm four young herons. Gray-wing turned to Mother Heron and nodded his head. Without making a sound he seemed to tell her:

"All is safe here at our nest. So let's fly back to the pond and catch some more food for our young ones!"

NATA'S FIRST FLIGHTS

Nata, the dragonfly, sat on a cattail leaf. Sunshine warmed her body and made her wings strong. When they were strong enough, Nata would sail away to catch mosquitoes for lunch.

Nata never had flown before. Until that morning, her home had been in the pond. She hatched there from an egg that her mother dropped when she swooped close to the water. The egg, which was in a waterproof case, sank to the bottom of the pond. There it lay for more than two weeks, until Nata was ready to hatch.

When Nata crawled out of the egg case, she did not look like a dragonfly. She was a tiny gray creature with a rough, prickly-looking body. She had two huge, dark eyes made of many six-sided sections called facets. Her wings were only small pads on her back, and her jointed legs resembled six tiny sticks.

The lower part of Nata's face was covered with something that looked very much like a mask. This mask really was her jointed lower lip, which had sharp hooks at the end. These hooks did not show, however, when the lip was against Nata's face.

People who know dragonflies say that Nata was a nymph. In olden times, nymphs were supposed to be goddesses who lived in trees, in hills, and in the water. Water nymphs could come out on land and talk to human beings.

Nata, of course, was not a goddess, but was just a young insect. She had to stay in the pond, where she walked about slowly or sat among stems and rubbish where she could not be seen. Sometimes she climbed a stem or a stick. There she sat as if she were waiting for something to happen.

Nata really was hungry and was waiting for food. Instead of going out to hunt, she always sat quietly until food came near her. Then all she had to do was reach out and catch it.

Nata did not catch food with her feet, but with her lower lip. She liked other insects, worms, tadpoles, and even tiny fish. When one of these creatures came near, her lip shot out like a flash. The hooks on the end closed and pulled the food into Nata's mouth. She bit it to pieces with jaws that worked up and down. She ate so fast that she was ready for the next worm or wriggler that came within her reach.

Nata could walk with her six legs, and she could swim from one place to another. She swam by pumping water into the back part of her body and squirting it out as hard as she could. Each squirt pushed her forward, just as pushing will move a boat. It wasn't a very good way to swim, but it did take Nata to places where there was plenty to eat.

And what a lot Nata ate! She ate so much and grew so fast that she became too large for her skin. Soon it began to split down the back. Nata then crawled out of the split place, with a new and larger skin.

This happened again and again as Nata kept on growing. She also became much more active. She could run as well as walk, and she felt hungry all the time. From morning till night she prowled through the pond, catching insects, worms, and tadpoles. She even captured young crayfish and minnows with the hooks on her lower lip.

One day Nata herself had a narrow escape

from being eaten. She was watching a young tadpole that might come near enough to be caught. She did not notice a hungry, yellow perch, which also was hunting for food. Down it came with its mouth open. Nata managed to dodge under a stick just as the fish snapped at the place where she had been.

Some young dragonflies spend a year in the water, and some other kinds spend two years. But almost three years went by before Nata was ready to leave the pond and become a full-grown dragonfly.

By this time she was large and brown, with a row of sharp spines on each side. She did not know that her body was starting to change under her hard brown skin. Changes were taking place, however, and they made Nata very tired. She was too tired to walk, swim, or eat. Instead, she sat quietly on the bottom of the pond.

At last a bright, warm morning came, and Nata felt better. She moved her body and her legs. Soon she walked to a cattail and began to climb.

Nata climbed and climbed until she was out of the water. Then she stopped and took a firm hold on a cattail leaf. She pressed hooks on her feet into the leaf, so she could not fall off.

After resting again, Nata began to twist and jerk. The hard skin on her back split open; out came her head and body, and her six rough legs. Next she threw herself backward, so that more of her body came out. At last she took a new hold on the leaf and crept out of her old, split skin.

Nata now was a full-grown dragonfly, with four brand-new wings. But instead of spreading out, they hung like wet wads of paper. Nata had to sit very still while her wings became hard. She also had to keep them from touching the cattail leaves. If one wing had pressed against a leaf, it might have hardened in a twist, so she could not use it. And without four good, flat wings, Nata could not fly!

While her wings dried, she changed color.

Her body became green and blue, while her legs turned a shiny black. Her wings were clear and shiny. They looked as if they were made of cellophane on a network of veins, or supports.

As Nata became stronger, the green on her body began to glow. It looked as if she had a bright light that shone through her hard skin.

Nata's eyes soon began to glow, too. The glow showed the tiny parts, or facets, that made up each eye. Nata could look in all directions through these facets. She probably could see better than any other insect living near the pond.

She could see quite well enough to watch a swarm of little flies that were buzzing above the pond. They passed Nata several times while her wings were soft. They came again a few hours later, when her wings were ready to be used. With a buzzing whirr she darted into the air and began to chase them. She left her empty nymph skin hanging upon the cattail.

The little flies tried to dodge. But no matter how fast they went, Nata could dart ahead and catch them. She ate fly after fly, until she had swallowed all her stomach could hold.

When Nata stopped eating flies, she flew down to sun herself on a cattail. The warm sunshine made her feel so good that she soon darted into the air, going round and round in circles. Once she came close to a tree—but instead of dodging it she shifted her wings and flew directly backward. At another time, she "stood still" in the air. Then she saw some more flies and darted away to catch them.

Nata never again would hunt underwater, lying in wait for food. She would catch her meals in the air, as all full-grown dragonflies do. She might even go far from the pond, and not come back until she was ready to lay her own eggs and let them sink to the bottom of the water.

MOTHER CRAYFISH'S TWO HOMES

Mother Crayfish stopped beside a large stone in the creek that flowed into the pond. She had been looking for a home. A cave at one side of the stone was just the kind of place she needed.

The cave had to be cleaned out, because nothing had lived in it for almost a year. There was mud in one corner and a pile of pebbles in another. Mother Crayfish began to dig up the pebbles. When she had dug up seven or eight little stones, she picked them up and carried them away.

You could hold all those pebbles in one hand and have some room left over. But they made a big load for Mother Crayfish. She had to hold them with her pincers and her front feet, and she had to brace them against her chin. Then she walked away on three pairs of feet, till she found a good place to drop her load.

Mother Crayfish did this time after time, until her home was finished. It was a shallow cave, just big enough to hold her body. Her long feelers, called antennae (an ten′ee), reached outside, where they would touch anything that came near. Her strong pincers were right at the entrance, ready to nip any creature that tried to get into the cave.

Mother Crayfish rested a long time after finishing her home. But at last she began to feel hungry. How good a juicy earthworm would taste! She could find one near the bank of the creek. She might find some lazy tadpoles, too. They would taste just as good as earthworms, although they would be harder to catch.

Mother Crayfish did not think all this out, for crayfish cannot think. They just feel and then do whatever instinct makes them do. When Mother Crayfish felt hungry, instinct made her crawl out of the cave and start to hunt for her supper. This time she walked on all four pairs of her jointed feet. She also moved four pairs of paddles on the underside of her body. They helped her glide through the water. She did not make one ripple, or stir up one bit of mud.

Near the edge of the creek, she stopped and waved her feelers. Sure enough, an earthworm had tumbled into the creek and lay wriggling on the bottom. Nip! Nip! went Mother Crayfish's pincers. When the earthworm stopped wriggling, she began to eat it. How good it did taste!

She was too busy eating to notice Bobby and Ruth as they came to the bank of the creek. They watched her nibble bits of food, picking them off with her pincers and putting them into her mouth.

"Don't you suppose she can see us?" Ruth asked. "Maybe her eyes aren't good!"

"I guess they aren't," Bobby answered. "I'm going to put this stick into the water. Perhaps she will pinch it!"

Mother Crayfish did not see the stick, but she touched it with one of her feelers.

She did not wait to find out what it was. She just dropped what was left of the worm, spread her tail, and bent the back part of her body as quickly as she could. It worked like a strong oar, jerking her backward through the water. Jerk,

jerk, jerk she went, with her pincers and legs trailing. In a moment Mother Crayfish was hidden in her cave.

She was safe, but she still was hungry. She waited till the children went away and came out to hunt again. A fish had swallowed the last of her worm, so she had to hunt for young insects that lived in the water. She hunted still longer to find a fat tadpole. Mother Crayfish could have eaten two or three tadpoles, but when a fish swam near her she stopped hunting and hid among some dead sticks. Then she slipped away and hurried to her cave.

One day the crayfish sat on a stone, cleaning the swimming paddles on the underside of her body. For cleaners she used her two hind feet. They picked bits of dirt from the paddles and scraped away bits of slime. When the paddles were perfectly clean, Mother Crayfish covered them with waterproof glue that was made inside her body.

Now she was ready to lay her eggs. As they

76

were laid, Mother Crayfish fastened them to her paddles in bunches that looked like tiny bunches of grapes. They bobbed to and fro when she walked. But they fitted under her tail very nicely when she swam backward.

The eggs hung and bobbed until they hatched. When baby crayfish came out of the eggs, they caught hold of the fringes on their mother's paddles. There they clung, catching food which they found as their mother carried them about.

Soon after the little crayfish grew pincers, they were able to take care of themselves. Still, they did not want to go away from their mother and find their own homes. They kept hold of the paddles just as long as they could.

Mother Crayfish knew how to make them let go. She jerked her body very hard, and off came the largest youngsters. She waited a while, jerked again, and off came many more. Soon the last little crayfish dropped off. It hid under some dead leaves and sticks at the bottom of the creek.

When summer came, the creek partly dried

up. There still were pools where her little ones
could live, but pools did not please Mother Crayfish. She left her cave and walked down the creek
to a place where the bank was very low. Out and
over the bank she went, looking for a place where
the ground was very damp.

When she found a good spot, she started to
dig. Her pincers pulled out lumps of dirt. Then
the dirt became sticky mud, which Mother Crayfish piled in a round "chimney." She kept on
digging until water trickled into her hole. When

the water covered her body, she stopped and took a long rest.

Ruth and Bobby found the mud "chimney" that Mother Crayfish had made. "I'll bet it's a snake hole!" said Ruth. "I'll bet it isn't," Bobby answered. "I'll bet it's the crayfish's summer home. She comes here to live when the creek goes dry. If we could reach to the bottom of the hole, we'd find her. She'd be all ready to nip our fingers with her big pincer-claws!"

DIVER AND FATHER GREBE

Diver sat beside some cattails and watched Father Grebe, her mate. He swam round and round her, flapping his wings. "Coo, coooo!" he called softly. "Come and swim with me!"

Diver and her mate were pied-billed grebes, though people sometimes called them dabchicks. Like all grebes, they were very good swimmers. They had short, strong legs and long-toed feet with big skinny webs, or lobes. Their legs were near the end of their bodies, where they could work like oars near the end of a boat.

The two pied-billed grebes also were very good divers. Sometimes they "stood" in the water and went down headfirst, in a great hurry. Sometimes they sank slowly, going down . . . down . . . down until they were out of sight. Then they swam away underwater. They could go halfway across the pond before coming up for breath.

Both Diver and Father Grebe liked to swim underwater when they were looking for food. They ate soft parts of plants and a few seeds, as well as minnows, tadpoles, and crayfish. They also ate many leeches, which Bobby called bloodsuckers. "I'm glad they do that," he told Ruth, "because I don't like bloodsuckers. They get on my legs when I go wading, and I have to pull them off!"

One day in early May, Diver and Father Grebe built their nest. They used dead cattail leaves, broken stems, and bunches of marsh grass. They fastened the longest, strongest pieces to living cattail plants. Then they piled on short pieces and even a little mud. In the end, their nest looked like a pile of rubbish that floated on the water.

Soon after the nest was built, Diver laid an egg in it. She laid another every day until there were six eggs in her floating nest.

Some people think that Diver covered her eggs with rubbish and then let the sun keep them warm. But she really did not do that at all. As soon as her six eggs were laid, Diver began to sit on them, warming them with her body. When she went away to swim or hunt food, Father Grebe often climbed onto the nest and sat on the eggs in her place.

Sometimes, of course, both grebes had to leave their nest. Then the last one to go did cover the eggs with dead leaves and mud. This kept crows and other hungry creatures from seeing the eggs and eating them while Diver and her mate were gone.

When the grebes left their nest, they never swam straight to the center of the pond. Often they dodged among the cattails, going to and fro until they were far from their home. If something alarmed them, they stopped and sat so still that they seemed to disappear. Their brownish black backs looked like the dark water, while the black on their necks seemed to be shadows made by the cattail leaves.

At other times, the grebes dived. They slipped from their nest without making a sound. Then they swam away underwater, where they could not be seen. When they did bob up to the surface, no one could tell where they had been.

Diver's eggs were about two thirds as long as a hen's egg. They were dull and pure white when she laid them, but mud and decaying plants stained them brown. Soon they seemed like part of the nest. A crow could have looked at them without knowing what they were.

The stains were not pretty, but they did not harm the eggs. Day after day the eggs changed and developed, until there were six baby grebes inside the dirty shells.

The first baby hatched twenty-five days after Diver began to sit. Chip-chip! went the baby grebe's beak, picking a hole through the shell. After a while, the shell broke into two pieces. Then out came Diver's first chick.

One egg hatched that day, and five eggs hatched the next. The chicks were tiny, downy babies with black and white stripes. Each one had a brown ring around its beak almost like its mother's.

As soon as each chick hatched, Mother Diver picked up the empty shell. She took it away, broke it to pieces, and dropped them into the water. They sank to the bottom of the pond. There no hungry prowler could see them and come to catch the chicks.

While Diver was breaking the last empty shell, two daring chicks wriggled to the edge of the nest. Tip—tip—then over the edge they went, right into the pond. Though they had never been in the water before, they began to move their legs and their little webbed feet. The first strokes sent them across the water to a cattail stem. There they stayed while their mother slipped off the nest and carried bits of shell away.

As Diver hurried back to the nest, she saw that one chick was tired. She swam close to him

and then stopped. The chick moved his legs and wriggled onto her back. There he snuggled down in her dark feathers.

Just then two boys with a dog came to the shore of the pond. They did not see Diver and her chick, but one boy threw a stick into the water and told the dog to fetch it. "Bow-wow!" the dog answered, and splashed into the pond.

Diver did not wait to find out what the dog was doing. As soon as it barked she dived, swimming underwater with the chick on her back. There it stayed until Diver came up for air. Then the chick shook itself and slipped off. It did not seem one bit surprised by its trip.

Though the little grebes could swim and dive, they did not look like their parents. Their downy coats were striped with black and white, and each one had a small red spot at the back of its head. The chicks looked like streaks of sunlight and shadow when they swam to and fro among the arrowheads and cattails.

One day Diver, the chicks, and Father Grebe

were swimming near the nest. Suddenly a huge green thing appeared on the water. The birds did not know that this was a boat, nor did they know that Ruth and Bobby were sitting near the pointed front end. They did know that the big green thing moved swiftly. They also heard it give a squeak as two long objects (the oars) moved upward and down again.

Mother Diver and her chicks dived, sinking into the water without making a ripple. Then they swam under the surface, as fast as they could go. Soon they were far away, hiding among the plants at the end of the pond.

Father Grebe did not dive—not even when the boat came near and Bobby shouted, "Look!" Instead, the old grebe flipped his feet and flashed the silvery feathers on his sides. He began to swim round and round, flapping and splashing as if he wanted to fly but could not get out of the water. "He's hurt!" Bobby told Ruth. "He's hurt and can't get away!"

"No, he isn't," Ruth answered. "He's only

trying to fool us. His mate and babies are not far away. Father Grebe is splashing and swimming while they go off to hide!"

Bobby did not think so—but suddenly Father Grebe disappeared. Down he went like a stone, except that he did not sink to the bottom. Both Ruth and Bobby saw him stop for a moment. Then his webbed feet spread out and moved backward, almost like the oars of a boat. Away went the grebe through the water, until he was out of sight.

"I guess you're right, Ruth," Bobby admitted. "The grebe wasn't hurt at all. He was just trying to fool us!"

"He did fool you, too," said their father, from the place where he sat as he rowed the boat. "You were so busy watching that one noisy bird that you didn't even look for Mother Diver and her chicks. They had a fine chance to swim away and hide in some other part of the pond.

"But don't let that worry you, Bobby. You have learned something about pied-billed grebes.

Next time you'll know what to look for when one old bird makes a fuss. Then you will see his mate and the young ones before they can get away!"

MUD PUPPIES IN THE POND

Bobby, Ruth, and some of their friends were wading in the creek. Mother Kingfisher rattled at them crossly. "She wants us to go away," said Ruth. "She wants us to go away so she can catch some fish!"

"I'm not go—" one of the boys began. Then he shouted, "Run! Here comes a big lizard! Run, or it will bite!"

Ruth knew that most lizards do not swim, and that only a few lizards can bite hard enough to hurt people. So she stood still and looked into the water. Sure enough; the creature was not a lizard at all, but a mud puppy. Ruth could see its long body, its wide, flat tail, and its four stubby legs.

Real puppies are little dogs, but mud puppies are distant relatives of frogs and toads. They have

slimy skins without scales and little round eyes, and are one to two feet long. Their color is greenish brown with black spots and mottlings. When they lie still they look very much like mud on the bottom of a river or pond.

The mud puppy came so near that Ruth and Bobby could see its gills. They looked like tufts of dark red moss growing out of the creature's neck. The mud puppy used its gills to breathe oxygen that was in the water. Blood that flowed through the gills took up, or absorbed, oxygen and carried it through the creature's body.

Frogs and toads have gills when they are young and live in the water as tadpoles. When they grow up they develop lungs, and their gills disappear. But mud puppies never really grow up. At least, they never change from gills to lungs or breathe oxygen from the air, even though they become much larger than any frog or toad. The mud puppy in the creek was fifteen inches long.

As the animal swam past, one of the boys tried

to catch it. He did get his hands around it, but the creature swished its broad tail and quickly got away. Its skin was covered with a thick coat of slime. This let it slip through the boy's hands when he tried to hold it.

The mud puppy went on down the creek until it came to the pond. There it swam to and fro, poking its blunt nose into corners among lily stems and pondweeds. At last it stopped beside a rotting log that lay on the bottom. Here was a fine sheltered place in which to hide. The mud puppy picked out a dark corner and snuggled down. Its brownish green skin looked so much like mud that a crayfish did not see it at all.

The mud puppy saw the crayfish, however, and watched it as it came toward the log. Once it stopped to catch a water insect. Then it spied a worm near the log and came closer. It was all ready to catch that worm—but just then the mud puppy caught the crayfish! It broke the crayfish's shell and ate its meat. Then it caught and ate the worm. This big lunch was very welcome after its long swim!

Still, the mud puppy did not like to hunt food during the bright part of the day. Soon it swam back to the log and slipped into its shady corner. There it lay through the whole afternoon. Now and then it moved its head or its tail, and once or twice it yawned. Except for these movements, however, it lay perfectly still.

When evening came, the mud puppy yawned again and swam out to find some supper. It ate several young water insects and a couple of snails. It also caught three fat tadpoles and swallowed them hungrily.

Those fat tadpoles were baby frogs, but other tadpoles that lived in the pond were young mud puppies. These creatures were long and slender, with four stubby legs. Each of their front feet had four toes, but their hind feet had five. They looked very much as they would when they became full grown.

Those tadpoles had hatched from eggs that a

mother mud puppy laid early in May. She put each egg on a long, tough stem and glued it to a stone where the water was almost five feet deep. She fastened about sixty eggs to the stone and then went away. When her babies hatched, they would take care of themselves, just as frog tadpoles did.

This mother mud puppy lived in an old bucket that someone had thrown into the pond. She found it one evening when she was hunting and suddenly swam close to Gray-wing, the heron. She just had time to dart into the bucket when the heron's beak shot into the water. *Thump!* it went against the bucket. But Gray-wing could not reach the mud puppy in her safe hiding place.

For several days the mother mud puppy hid under the bucket and hunted not far away. But one evening she tried to catch some minnows that swam away toward another part of the pond. On and on the mud puppy went, till she came to the farthest part of the pond. There she found the sunken log, and beside it she saw the head of another mud puppy—the one that Ruth and Bobby had seen. Since he was at one side of the log, she went to the other. There she found a dark hole, surrounded by plants that would hide her from herons and other hungry creatures.

Now both mud puppies made their homes beside the log. On sunny days they stayed in the dark shadows, where even crayfish could not see them. On cloudy days they came out and rested beside the log. Often they half lay and half floated, with their tails and hind legs on the mud while their forelegs and heads swayed to and fro in the water. They could lie like that for hours, as if they were asleep or just too lazy to move.

Although the mud puppies lived so near one another, they never were really friendly. They did not swim together or play games and they did not share their food. When the mother mud puppy disappeared one night, the other one did not seem to be surprised, nor did he try to find her. Instead, he swam straight to his side of the log and settled down in the shadows to rest for another day.

After all, he had enough to eat, and his hollow beside the log was a pleasant place to stay. Why should he bother about another mud puppy that he hadn't known very well and might never see again?

RED-WINGS FROM THE SOUTH

"Oka-lee! Oka-lee-ee!" sang Red-wing as he teetered on a cattail stalk. When he sang he spread his tail feathers and raised his wings. This made him look larger than he really was. It also flashed the bright red spot that covered each of his shoulders.

Red-wing had just come back to the pond after spending the winter months in the South. He returned one morning in early April, with a big flock of red-winged blackbirds. When they saw the pond they swooped down, flew in a circle, and then perched on bushes, dead weeds, and stalks of last year's cattails.

After they had rested a while, the blackbirds began to choose homes for the summer. Red-wing picked out a part of the pond where there were many cattail stalks. It looked like several

other places, but Red-wing thought it just right. "Oka-lee! Oka-lee!" he called, spreading his wings. "This is mine!" he seemed to be saying. "Other blackbirds must keep away!"

Although Red-wing wanted his home for himself, he was not unfriendly. He chattered with his blackbird neighbors. When he felt hungry he joined their flock and went to eat weed seeds in fields far away from the pond.

Two whole weeks went by before Mother Blackbird also came to the pond. She flew down quietly and perched among the cattails near her mate.

Mother Blackbird did not look at all like Red-wing. His feathers were shiny black, with bright red on each shoulder and buff below the red. She had no red on her shoulders, and the rest of her feathers were brownish and gray, with dark and light stripes. She was very hard to see when she perched quietly among the cattails.

For a few days, Red-wing did not seem to be glad that Mother Blackbird had come. Then he began to follow her and sing songs to her. One sunny morning he sang his "Oka-lee" song over and over again, lifting his wings and spreading his tail. Then he flew into the air, going round and round until he was high above the pond. Soon he partly closed his wings and dived down toward Mother Blackbird.

"He's showing off," Bobby told Ruth as they stood on the bank to watch. "O-o-oh, just look at him now!"

Red-wing had dived and then soared into the air. There he fluttered his wings rapidly while the red on his shoulders showed brightly. At the same time, he called, "Chek-chek-chek!" as loudly as he could. Although he seemed to be scolding, his calls pleased Mother Blackbird very much.

On the first day of May, Red-wing and his mate began to build their nest. Really, Red-wing perched on a cattail to sing and keep watch, while Mother Blackbird gathered dry leaves and grass and wove them into a basket. Although it looked rough and weak, she fastened it very tightly to the cattail leaves.

When this part of the nest was woven, Mother Blackbird brought bits of dead wood and other rubbish. She used these to fill open spaces, making the nest solid. Then she gave it a lining of tough marsh grass and some hair that she had found on a fence near the pond. She knew that the hair made good nest lining, but she didn't know that it came from the tail of Ruth's and Bobby's pony.

"That gives us a share in the nest," Ruth told Bobby. "A bigger share than Red-wing deserves, 'cause all he did was to watch her and sing!"

After her nest was completed, Mother Blackbird laid four eggs in it. Some of her neighbors laid only three, and others laid five. But four eggs seemed just the right number for Mother Blackbird to lay.

Red-wing called, "Chek-chek!" when he saw the eggs, which were about one inch long. Their shells were pale blue in color, with streaks and

spots of dark brownish purple near the larger end. Red-wing admired every egg, and sat near by to watch them when Mother Blackbird flew away to eat lunch.

One day, soon after she had gone, Red-wing saw something move in the cattails near his home. Soon he spied a small brown-and-black marsh wren with a long, curved beak. It dodged from one plant to another, and then hopped to the edge of the nest. It was ready to break the shell of an egg and drink the yellow inside!

As Red-wing saw the wren hop to the nest he screamed, "Tsee-ay!" angrily. Down he came with his sharp beak open—but by that time the wren was scurrying away. It slipped from plant to plant so fast that Red-wing could not catch it. With a scream that plainly said, "Keep away!" he went back to keep watch against other enemies. There he was when Mother Blackbird came back to perch on a leaf before settling down in the nest.

Ten days after the last egg was laid, the first

ones began to hatch. Out came the red-wing babies, one after another. At last four of them were lying in the basket nest.

The babies did not look like Red-wing, and they did not look like Mother Blackbird. They were little, with bright red skins and tufts of down instead of feathers. Their eyes were tightly closed, and they opened their mouths very wide when they asked for food.

Both Mother Blackbird and Red-wing began to hunt insects that floated on the water or flew among the cattails. As soon as they caught a mouthful of insects, the old birds went home to feed their hungry babies. They never gave the little ones seeds or grain. Even the old birds now ate insects instead of other food.

Day after day the red-winged blackbirds fed their babies, and day after day the little ones grew. Soon their bodies and wings became covered with feathers that looked very much like Mother's. When they were nine days old, they could flutter their wings. On the tenth day, they climbed out of the nest and perched side by side on a cattail stalk that leaned over the water.

Red-wing saw them go and watched to protect them from danger. Mother Blackbird was away hunting. When she came back, she started to go to the nest. Then she heard the little ones on their perch, and quickly flew to them.

As she came, every baby opened its mouth and began to cry for food. She fed the one that begged hardest, putting the food so far down his throat that nothing could wriggle out. Then both she and Red-wing flew away to find food for their other babies.

"Red-wing and Mother Blackbird will do this for two or three more weeks," Father told Ruth and Bobby. "Then the young blackbirds will be strong enough to take care of themselves. They will go away to live and hunt insects in another part of the pond."

"Will Mother Blackbird rest when they are gone?" asked Ruth.

"She may rest," Father answered, "but only

for a day or two. Then she'll gather grass and dead leaves and use them to make another nest. When it is ready, she will lay some more eggs and sit on them until they hatch. Then she and Red-wing will have to take care of a new family.

"They can't stop work until these new babies are grown and are ready to find food without help from their mother and father. That means that Red-wing and Mother Blackbird will be busy for a long, long time!"

LIMNA AND A MUSSEL

Limna, the pond snail, made her home among plants that grew in the water. She often climbed the stems of lilies or crawled on their big, flat leaves. She also climbed the pondweeds to eat their leaves for lunch.

Limna had a shell that was coiled round and round. One end of the coil was pointed, but the other end was oval. The oval end was open, and was big enough to let her soft body slip out and in again. Her shell was yellowish brown outside. The color of the inside did not show, for Limna's body hid it.

When the pond snail crawled, she stretched her soft body out of her shell. This showed her blunt head, with two long feelers and eyes that could just tell daylight from darkness. Limna used her feelers to find out where to go. Her foot, which she used to climb and crawl, was the flat underside of her body.

Limna's mouth was near the front of her foot. That may seem queer to you, but it really was a good arrangement. When she crawled across the leaf of a pondweed she could stick out her tongue and scrape off bits of leaf to eat. She couldn't have done that if her mouth had been on her head!

Limna liked to eat leaves, but she also ate other kinds of food. Sometimes she caught tiny worms or young insects that lived in the pond. When she covered a worm or insect with her foot, it could not get away. Then she scraped and scraped with her tongue until her prey was eaten.

Most snails can breathe oxygen in water, but Limna needed air. She would go to the surface of the pond, catch a big bubble of air, and store it in a pocket of her moist, slimy skin. Then she would go underwater again. The bubble of air would last her a long time, even when she was crawling and eating.

Limna often met wheel snails as she crawled
here and there in the pond. Their brown shells
were flat and closely coiled, and were almost as
round as wheels. Their feet were much wider
than Limna's, but their feelers were short and
slender.

Many wheel snails often lived together, sitting

quietly on the bottom or crawling about for food. They also ate leaves, but they crawled so slowly that they seldom caught insects or worms.

One day, while Limna was resting, Bobby waded into the pond. He watched some wheel snails as they crawled about very, very slowly. Then he picked up a greenish brown mussel, which he called a clam. Its thick shell was not coiled like a snail's, but was made of two parts called valves. These were fastened together by a hinge that looked like dark celluloid. A thin layer that also looked like celluloid covered the outer surface of the shell. The inner surface, which Bobby could not see, was lined with a pearly layer.

Bobby tried to open the shell, but the mussel held it shut. Bobby began to pry, but still the shell remained closed. At last he threw the mussel back into the pond. Why keep an animal that seemed as hard and as dead as a stone?

For a while the mussel lay just where she fell, on the bottom of the pond. Then she opened her shell and thrust out a thick pink foot. The foot reached into the mud and tugged. It tugged until the mussel stood up, with the edges of its shell in the mud.

Tugging seemed to be hard work, for the mussel stopped to rest. Then she thrust her foot forward and began to pull. Each thrust and pull made her shell bob and slip forward. Bob–slip, bob–slip, it went, leaving a track that looked as if a stick had been dragged in the mud.

The mussel had no head, no eyes, and no feelers, and most of her body was covered by shell. She could not tell where she was going, or what was in the way. Sometimes she bumped into stones. Once she started around a log but got lost. She crawled round and round in circles and then went in a new direction, instead of going around the log.

After crawling for a long time, the mussel became hungry. She partly burrowed into the mud by reaching and pulling with her foot. Then she put out two narrow tubes that had rings of

wriggly things that looked like hairs at the ends. She brought water into one tube and sent it out through the other. Hundreds of tiny plants and animals floated in the water that came into the tube. The mussel caught these things and ate them before sending the water out again.

While the mussel was eating, a thirsty cow waded into the pond. It stirred up sticks, dead leaves, and mud. When mud touched the mussel's "hairs," she closed both tubes and pulled them back. Then she closed her shell tightly, protecting her body from harm.

One spring day the mussel laid several hundred eggs. Instead of putting the eggs in a nest she kept them in the folds of her soft body. There they hatched into tiny creatures with slender, whiplike tails.

Soon after the little ones hatched, Mother Mussel sent them out into the pond through one of her two tubes. Instead of crawling about on the bottom, the babies began to swim by jerking their whiplike tails. Here and there they went swimming until they met a minnow, a bullhead or some other fish. In a jiffy the babies fastened themselves to the fish and let it carry them away.

The baby mussels stayed on the fish until they were partly grown. By that time they had thin shells and were able to take care of themselves. One by one they dropped from the fish and settled in the mud. There they began to crawl about, just as their mother had done.

Some of the young ones lived near their mother, but others were far away, at the opposite side of the pond. A few were not in the pond at all. While they were fastened to minnows and bullheads, the fish had swum out of the pond and up the little creek. A few went as much as a mile, and one minnow went even farther. When young mussels dropped from that minnow, they lay in a pool almost three miles from the pond in which they had hatched.

That was a long way to travel—much farther than a full-grown mussel could go in its whole lifetime!

THE STORY OF CROAKER GREEN FROG

"Krr-rung! Krr-rr-rung!" sang the frogs one night early in April. "Spring is here!" they seemed to be saying. "Spring is here! Yes, spring's here!"

Several different frogs were singing, in different parts of the pond. The bullfrogs were biggest of all, and when they sang, "Krr-err-RUNG!" their voices were hoarse and loud. The spotted leopard frogs sang more softly, puffing out pouches of skin on each side of their heads. The green frogs called, "Krr-rung!" over and over again. They sang so hard that their sides swelled up and their bodies jerked to and fro.

The green frog that sang hardest of all sat on the end of a log that was lying in the water. He was singing to his mate, who had hopped to a stone beside some dead cattails.

Green Frogs

It was not hard to tell Mr. Green Frog from his mate. Both had bright green heads and shoulders, olive-colored backs, and dark spots on their sides. But he had an orange-yellow throat, while Mrs. Green Frog's throat was white with dark gray markings. Her ears also were much smaller than his. Mr. Green Frog's ears were round and flat, and larger than his eyes.

When morning came, the two frogs swam until they came to a branch that had fallen into the pond. There they stopped, and Mrs. Green Frog began to lay her eggs.

When a mother bird lays eggs, she generally puts them into a nest where she can protect them and keep them warm. But Mrs. Green Frog's eggs did not need a nest, for she covered them with thick jelly and fastened them to the branch. The jelly would keep the eggs from floating away, while sunshine would keep them warm until they were ready to hatch.

There were almost four thousand eggs in the jelly that Mrs. Green Frog fastened to the

Leopard Frogs

branch. Each egg was a little ball, dark brown on its upper part and white at the bottom.

The brown part of each egg soon began to change and grow. In three days it became a dark-colored tadpole with an oval body and a tiny, wriggly tail. Boys and girls who came to the pond often called these tadpoles "pollywogs."

The tadpoles hatched quite easily, just by wriggling out of the jelly. But instead of swimming away, they fastened themselves to the jelly with suckers under their chins. There they stayed until their mouths developed, and they were ready to eat.

Though the tadpoles were baby frogs, they did not look one bit like their father and mother. Their mouths were very small, and they still had no eyes, legs, or nostrils. They breathed by soaking up air that was in the water through tiny things called gills. These gills looked a bit like two bunches of leaves behind each tadpole's head.

The first tadpole to swim away from the jelly

was one we shall call Croaker. He wriggled his tail very hard and swam to a last year's weed stem that was standing in the pond. When he reached the stem he caught hold of it with his suckers and settled down to rest.

Soon Croaker's brothers and sisters also began to swim away from the jelly. A few of them—not more than a hundred—followed him to the weed stem. Many more wriggled their way to cattail stalks or to twigs, and some dived to the bottom of the pond. Wherever they went, they met tadpole babies that had hatched from eggs laid by other green frogs. Soon all of them were mixed together, until even the tadpoles themselves could not tell which was which.

When the tadpoles had finished resting, they began to eat. Their food was tiny plants called algae (al'jee) that grew in thin layers on dead weeds, cattail stalks, and other things in the pond. The tadpoles wriggled their tails and bobbed their heads as they nibbled the algae.

Some creatures eat and then rest a long time

before they eat again. But Croaker and his neighbors did not do that. They ate and ate all day long, and probably they ate at night. If something disturbed them and made them stop, they soon began to eat again.

So much food made Croaker Tadpole grow and change rapidly. Two dark spots on his head turned into eyes, while a fold of skin at the back of his head spread out until it covered his gills. His mouth let water come in to his gills, while a hole on his left side let it go out again.

Although Croaker changed so much, he still was not a frog. His mouth was small and so were his eyes, and he had no ears at all. He also had no arms or legs, which meant that he could not sit down or jump away from danger. Instead, he used his tail, which developed a long skinny fin on its upper and under sides. When Croaker moved his tail quickly, he could swim through the water as fast as many little fish.

Croaker met many dangerous creatures as he swam about the pond. First came the water

Bullfrog

tigers, which liked to catch and eat small tadpoles as much as they liked to eat fairy shrimps. There also were hungry dragonfly nymphs and big brown water bugs. Both liked to eat tadpoles, but Croaker escaped them by dodging and swimming as fast as he could go.

Croaker also hurried away every time he came near a bullfrog. Bullfrogs always were hungry, and they didn't seem to care what they ate. They swallowed the big brown water bugs, as well as crayfish, diving beetles, snails, and small fish. When they could, they also ate tadpoles, and even other frogs. Once Croaker saw a bullfrog that had swallowed a leopard frog headfirst. It was too big to be gobbled down at one gulp, so the bullfrog sat with the leopard frog's legs sticking out of his mouth!

All summer long Croaker ate, swam, and escaped his hungry neighbors. But when autumn came and the water grew cold, he began to feel dull. At last he went to the bottom of the pond and wriggled down into the mud. There he lay without moving until spring came again.

Croaker spent his second summer much as he spent the first one. But a really great adventure began when he was two years old.

By that time he was a big, fat tadpole with a greenish back and with white on the underside of his body. Soon two little lumps appeared beside his tail. The lumps became longer

and larger, till they turned into hind legs and feet.

While Croaker's legs grew at the back of his body, his arms began to grow inside it. Soon his left arm came out through the hole that took water away from his gills. The right arm had no hole, so it pushed its way out through Croaker's skin.

After that, changes came almost every day. Croaker's mouth became wider, and ears appeared at the back of his head. His eyes grew larger, too, but his tail became shorter and shorter. When it finally disappeared, Tadpole Croaker turned into a frog.

No one knows how Croaker felt when that happened, for he could not tell. But he did begin to do many things he never had done before. He hopped out of water onto land, and dived into the water again. When something alarmed him, he jumped high before diving and gave a loud yelp. That yelp meant "Danger!" to every other frog in the pond.

Croaker also began to eat flies, grasshoppers, and insects of other kinds. He caught them by flipping out his sticky tongue and flipping it in again. His tongue went out and back so fast that insects almost never got away.

At last there came a spring when Croaker was

five years old. By that time he was three inches long, and was one of the largest green frogs in the pond. He also could sing, "Kr-rr-rung!" louder than any of his green frog neighbors.

One evening while Croaker was singing he met White-throat, his mate. She sat quietly while he sang to her, as if she liked his song.

When morning came, Croaker and White-throat swam to a bush that hung down into the water. There White-throat laid her thousands of eggs and covered them with jelly. When that was done, she and Croaker quickly swam away. Their eggs would hatch without being cared for. Why, then, should the parent frogs watch them or bother the tadpoles when they hatched?